Count
YOUR
Rainbows

Count YOUR Rainbows

A GRATITUDE JOURNAL

Jenny Mecher

Adams Media
New York London Toronto Sydney New Delhi

Adams Media
An Imprint of Simon & Schuster, Inc.
57 Littlefield Street
Avon, Massachusetts 02322

For information about special discounts for bulk purchases, please contact Simon & Schuster Special Sales at 1-866-506-1949 or business@simonandschuster.com.

The Simon & Schuster Speakers Bureau can bring authors to your live event. For more information or to book an event contact the Simon & Schuster Speakers Bureau at 1-866-248-3049 or visit our website at www.simonspeakers.com.

Interior design by Sylvia McArdle
Interior illustrations by Jenny Mecher

Manufactured in the United States of America

10 9 8 7 6 5 4 3 2

Library of Congress Cataloging-in-Publication Data has been applied for.

ISBN 978-1-5072-1127-4

"thank you." You might look to small things—your delicious coffee, your favorite book or song—or big things—the beautiful sky, your family. You'll also consider your life—past, present, and future—and make time to acknowledge all the people, places, and things you have to be grateful for.

There's no one "right way" to practice gratitude. Some days, you might find it most beneficial to do something alone, such as writing or drawing. Other times, taking outward action might resonate strongly for you—maybe you reach out to a few old friends to say how happy you are to have them in your life. This journal gives you a variety of ways, big and small, to incorporate gratitude into your day and your state of mind.

Everyone experiences rain showers in life now and then. But if you teach yourself to see the rainbows that follow them, you will feel more joyful, relaxed, and hopeful. And when you stop and truly appreciate those rainbows, a magical thing happens: you see more and more of them!

List five "little things" that you're thankful for right now, at this very moment.

Walk as if you are KISSING THE EARTH with your feet.

THICH NHAT HANH

Get outside today, even if it's just for a few minutes. Make a mental note of something you enjoy about being outdoors. Maybe the sun on your skin, the wind on your face, or the smell of the air. Write about it.

_____

_____

_____

_____

_____

_____

_____

_____

_____

_____

_____

_____

_____

_____

_____

_____

_____

_____

_____

_____

_____

_____

_____

_____

_____

Gratitude is all about choosing to believe that the good stuff in your life is abundant. Consider these ways to think about abundance in your life:

- What are some words or images that pop up when you think of the word *abundance*? Describe them, or draw them if you're feeling artsy!

- What areas of your life feel particularly abundant with goodness right now? Your answer could be as simple as "My fridge is full of nutritious food."

- Fill the basket by drawing fruits, flowers, or hearts until it is overflowing.

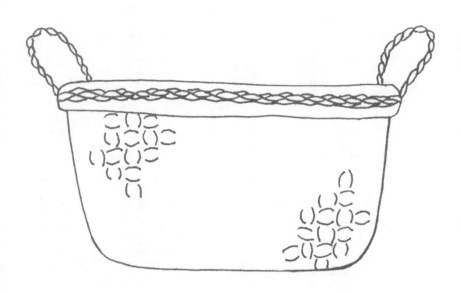

$\top$oday is a new day. New days bring new possibilities.

_____

_____ pleasantly surprised me today.

Today I learned _____

_____ .

_____

_____ completely amazed me today.

Today I got to try _____

_____ .

_____

_____ was the most beautiful thing I saw today.

Today I was able to eat _____

_____ .

_____

_____ made me laugh today.

Today made me especially grateful for _____

_____ .

This is a WONDERFUL day. I've never seen this one before.

MAYA ANGELOU

Do you remember making holiday or birthday wish lists as a kid? Writing long lists of gifts you hoped to receive? Try making a list of all the "gifts" you've already received in life. Write a little thank-you note next to each one.

When eating a fruit, think of the person who planted the tree.

VIETNAMESE PROVERB

Millions of people in the world live without adequate access to clean water. Today, take note every time that water is available to you, right inside your home or workplace, in public spaces, or outside. Write about it.

_____

_____

_____

_____

_____

_____

_____

_____

_____

_____

_____

_____

_____

_____

_____

_____

_____

_____

_____

_____

_____

_____

_____

It's a sign of mediocrity when you demonstrate gratitude with moderation.

ROBERTO BENIGNI

Take a walk around your living space. Pay attention to the things that you use almost every day but probably otherwise would never really think about. How do they make your life easier? Happier? More comfortable?

_____

_____

_____

_____

_____

_____

_____

_____

_____

_____

_____

_____

_____

_____

_____

_____

_____

_____

_____

_____

_____

"Thank you" is the BEST PRAYER that anyone could say.

ALICE WALKER

One of the best moments in life is when something happens that forces you to pause and say, "That is AMAZING." Write about something that has happened recently that has made you feel this way.

Write about something in your life that you could possibly consider a "miracle." Have you ever thought of it as being miraculous before? Does describing it as a miracle change how you feel about it?

_____

_____

_____

_____

_____

_____

_____

_____

_____

_____

_____

_____

_____

_____

_____

_____

_____

_____

_____

_____

_____

_____

_____

Start listing all of the good things in your life, and as the day goes on, add more as you think of them. How many can you come up with? Try to fill this whole page today.

_____

_____

_____

_____

_____

_____

_____

_____

_____

_____

_____

_____

_____

_____

_____

_____

_____

_____

_____

_____

_____

_____

_____

_____

_____

_____

_____

Give Thanks
for A LITTLE
and you will
find A LOT.

HAUSA PROVERB

Many times, the difference between a negative and a positive experience is determined by our perception. When was the last time you perceived a "glass half-empty" situation? Write it in the bottom of the glass. Now, fill in the bottom of the glass using a colored pencil, coloring over your "empty" words. How have you decided to see this as a "glass half-full" situation?

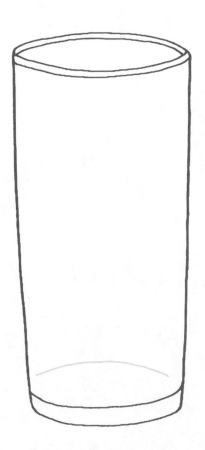

Write it on your heart that every day is the Best Day in the Year.

RALPH WALDO EMERSON

Think about the first time you heard your absolute favorite song, or the first time you ate at your favorite restaurant, or the first time you experienced something DIVINE. What did that feel like? What specific details can you remember about it? How did it make a difference in your life at the time?

_____

_____

_____

_____

_____

_____

_____

_____

_____

_____

_____

_____

_____

_____

_____

_____

_____

_____

_____

_____

_____

What thoughts or feelings do you have when you think of the word *enough*? What does it feel like to have "enough"?

Try to remember and write down the last three gifts you received from friends, coworkers, parents, or anyone else. In what ways were each of these gifts special and meaningful to you?

A man is but a product of his thoughts. What he thinks, he becomes.

GANDHI

Think about all of the clothes in your wardrobe. Then zero in on some of your favorite pieces. Do they make you feel cozy? Do they help you to unplug from a stressful day? Do they make you feel your cutest? What gratitude can you give for your clothes and how they make you feel?

_____

_____

_____

_____

_____

_____

_____

_____

_____

_____

_____

_____

_____

_____

_____

_____

_____

_____

_____

_____

Be thankful for what you have and you'll end up having more. If you concentrate on what you don't have, you will never, ever have enough.

OPRAH WINFREY

Have you noticed that the more you try to find things to be grateful for, the more there seem to be? Write down ten things (big or small) that you're thankful for this week that you may have never noticed before you started practicing gratitude.

_____

_____

_____

_____

_____

_____

_____

_____

_____

_____

_____

_____

_____

_____

_____

_____

_____

_____

_____

_____

_____

_____

_____

Set a timer for two minutes. Close your eyes and take deep breaths. What do you notice that you are thankful for when you make time to just breathe? Write it down.

_____

_____

_____

_____

_____

_____

_____

_____

_____

_____

_____

_____

_____

_____

_____

_____

_____

_____

_____

_____

_____

_____

What if you could regularly be in a "state of gratitude"? List three go-to practices you could add to your day to make gratitude part of your daily routine.

_____

_____

_____

_____

_____

_____

_____

_____

_____

_____

_____

_____

_____

_____

_____

_____

_____

_____

_____

_____

_____

_____

_____

Be in **LOVE** with your life, **EVERY** detail of it.

JACK KEROUAC

Write down five good things that have happened to you so far this week.

_____
_____
_____

I HAVE TO
REally ENjoy
THE Good Things
BECAUSE IT MAKES
THE BAD THINGS
OK.

EMMA WATSON

Have you ever thought about the relationship between gratitude and peace? Write down some thoughts or feelings you have when you think of the word *peace*. What do they have in common with feeling grateful?

_____

_____

_____

_____

_____

_____

_____

_____

_____

_____

_____

_____

_____

_____

_____

_____

_____

_____

_____

_____

_____

_____

Consider all of the unexpected twists and turns your life has taken so far. Choose one and write about why you're thankful that it happened to you.

_____

_____

_____

_____

_____

_____

_____

_____

_____

_____

_____

_____

_____

_____

_____

_____

_____

_____

_____

_____

_____

_____

_____

_____

Think about bedtime. Do you have a routine? Do you like to watch your favorite show in bed? Do you have especially cozy sheets? What about bedtime brings you comfort or joy?

_____

_____

_____

_____

_____

_____

_____

_____

_____

_____

_____

_____

_____

_____

_____

_____

_____

_____

_____

_____

_____

_____

_____

Gratitude is the memory of the heart.

JEAN BAPTISTE
MASSIEU

Write six things you LOVE about your life right now inside of these cute hearts.

Attitude is a little thing that makes a Big Difference.

WINSTON CHURCHILL

Celebrations like holidays and birthdays bring so many opportunities to practice gratitude, but it's so easy to become bogged down with (usually unrealistic) expectations. How can you approach these days with more appreciation than expectation?

Think about all of your life still ahead of you. Write down five things that you're looking forward to in the future.

What thoughts or feelings do you have when you think of the word *joy*? Have you noticed that practicing gratitude brings you more joy? Think of a time when you've made the connection between gratitude and joy and write about it.

_____

_____

_____

_____

_____

_____

_____

_____

_____

_____

_____

_____

_____

_____

_____

_____

_____

_____

_____

_____

_____

_____

I find ECSTASY
in LIVING—
the mere SENSE
of LIVING is
JOY enough.

EMILY DICKINSON

When you arise in the morning, think of what a precious privilege it is to be Alive— to breathe, to think, to enjoy, to love.

MARCUS AURELIUS

Think about your mornings. Do you have a routine? Do you wake up and look at your phone? Make coffee? Shower? List three simple practices you can make part of your morning routine to begin each day with a grateful mindset.

_____

_____

_____

_____

_____

_____

_____

_____

_____

_____

_____

_____

_____

_____

_____

_____

_____

_____

_____

_____

_____

_____

_____

Write down some words that describe you when you're in a good place. Joyful? Focused? Peaceful? Helpful? Go through the words and try to narrow them down to three essential words that describe you at your very best. Rewrite your three words at the bottom of the page (nice and pretty, if you like) to keep as a mantra.

Have you noticed any changes in your general attitude since practicing gratitude? Write a little bit about whatever changes you've noticed in your life.

_____

_____

_____

_____

_____

_____

_____

_____

_____

_____

_____

_____

_____

_____

_____

_____

_____

_____

_____

_____

_____

_____

_____

_____

_____

When I started counting my blessings, my WHole Life turned around.

WILLIE NELSON

List three things that made you feel frustrated this past week, leaving some space in between them. Now, next to each of them, list three things—no matter how small—that made you feel fortunate this week.

_____

_____
_____
_____
_____
_____
_____
_____
_____
_____
_____
_____
_____
_____
_____
_____
_____
_____
_____
_____
_____
_____
_____
_____

What are some different ways that you currently express gratitude? Writing it down? Saying "thank you"? Enjoying the outdoors? What are some new ways you'd like to try? Circle some ways here or add more of your own.

taking a photo

being creative

listening to music

praying

sending a thank-you note

saying thank you

writing it down

journaling

enjoying the outdoors

reflecting with a friend

paying it forward

meditating

At some point in life the WORLD'S BEAUTY becomes enough.

TONI MORRISON

What are the three most beautiful things you've seen this week? A sunrise on the way to work? A neighbor's garden on your afternoon run? The streetlights glowing on the way home from dinner? Write about them below.

Have you noticed how expressing your gratitude to others affects them? Write about one way a relationship has improved by you expressing your gratitude.

When you practice gratefulness, there is a sense of respect toward others.

DALAI LAMA

Pride can sometimes block the road to gratitude. Have you noticed that humility is an important part of your journey with gratitude? If so, how?

_____

_____

_____

_____

_____

_____

_____

_____

_____

_____

_____

_____

_____

_____

_____

_____

_____

_____

_____

_____

_____

_____

_____

_____

_____

Instead of complaining that the rosebush is full of thorns, be happy that the thorn bush has roses.

GERMAN PROVERB

Have you noticed that showing gratitude for the "little" things can affect your gratitude level for the "big" things? Do they seem bigger and better than they used to? How have your attitude and response changed when you experience a big win?

What in your life feels like a privilege right now? Are there people in your life whom you feel lucky to know? Are there parts of your job that you feel honored to be able to do? List them here.

Have you noticed a connection between gratitude and your happiness? Why do you think being grateful makes you feel happier?

_____
_____
_____
_____

_____
_____
_____
_____
_____
_____
_____
_____
_____
_____
_____
_____
_____
_____
_____
_____
_____
_____
_____
_____
_____

Happiness is not a goal, — it is a — by-product.

ELEANOR ROOSEVELT

Although there are some things that I don't like about my job, three things that I really appreciate about it are…

_____

_____

_____

_____

_____

_____

_____

_____

_____

_____

_____

_____

_____

_____

_____

_____

_____

_____

_____

_____

_____

_____

_____

Reflect upon your present blessings — of which every man has many — not on your past misfortunes, of which all men have some.

CHARLES DICKENS

I feel happiest when I am...

_____

_____

_____

_____

_____

_____

_____

_____

_____

_____

_____

_____

_____

_____

_____

_____

_____

_____

_____

_____

_____

_____

_____

Think of five things that make you happy. Write a thank-you note for each one here.

Many artists and performers say that gratitude transforms their art into something truly beautiful and meaningful. How do you express your creative side? How can you incorporate gratitude into your creative process? What do you appreciate about the whole experience of being creative?

_____

_____

_____

_____

_____

_____

_____

_____

_____

_____

_____

_____

_____

_____

_____

_____

_____

_____

_____

_____

_____

_____

_____

Gratitude opens the door to the power, the wisdom, the creativity of the universe. You open the door through gratitude.

DEEPAK CHOPRA

Using colored pencils or a calligraphy pen, write one thing below that you can be thankful for every morning when you wake up. (Feel free to make it beautiful and uplifting to look at.) You might write, "I'm thankful for another day" or "I'm thankful for my cozy apartment." Take a picture with your phone and make it your lock screen. Or make a copy and hang it in a place where you'll see it every day. Use it to help you start each day with gratitude.

Silent
gratitude
isn't very
much use
to anyone.

GERTRUDE STEIN

One way of practicing gratitude is doing nice things for others. What are three things you can do today for a friend or a stranger to pay it forward? Bring a friend a surprise coffee? Text a family member to say you appreciate him or her? Smile and say "good morning" to someone on the street?

_____

_____

_____

_____

_____

_____

_____

_____

_____

_____

_____

_____

_____

_____

_____

_____

_____

_____

_____

_____

_____

How do you react when something really sucky is going on in your life? Are you impatient with people? Do you wilt and binge-watch Netflix on your couch all weekend? Next time, try to turn those reactions around. Maybe call a friend and thank him or her for being there for you. Or go outside for a walk and listen to a motivating podcast. What changes can you make in times of stress to be more appreciative of all the good in your life? Write them here.

_____

_____

_____

_____

_____

_____

_____

_____

_____

_____

_____

_____

_____

_____

_____

_____

_____

_____

_____

Write about one life lesson that you've learned from a difficult experience in your life. What was particularly hard about it? What did you learn about yourself, and how did you come out of it a better person?

_____

_____

_____

_____

_____

_____

_____

_____

_____

_____

_____

_____

_____

_____

_____

_____

_____

_____

_____

_____

_____

_____

If everything
was perfect
you would
never learn
and you would
never grow.

BEYONCÉ KNOWLES

Look over this list of words. Which words describe you? Draw a heart around each of them, and embrace the messy beauty that is you!

considerate

OUTSPOKEN

ENERGETIC

courageous

EMPATHETIC

COMPASSIONATE

thoughtful

QUIET

loud

SASSY

FRIENDLY

charming

INTUITIVE

introspective

It's not what HAPPENS to you, but how you REACT that matters.

EPICTETUS

What do you think it is about the really hard times that seems to bring out the best in some people? Do you see this in yourself at all? What advantages do you see in hitting "rock bottom"? Write them down below, and refer back to them when you come to a time in your life that feels really trying.

_____

_____

_____

_____

_____

_____

_____

_____

_____

_____

_____

_____

_____

_____

_____

_____

_____

_____

_____

_____

_____

_____

_____

Write down some places in the country or the world that you've visited. What was the most beautiful thing you saw in each place? The most moving? The most interesting? In times when the world is getting you down, refer back to this page and remember all of the beauty you've seen in it.

Who are some people you appreciate who are far away? It might be a friend who's moved away, family back home, or an old teacher or professor. Write down their names below and list what you appreciate about them. When you're finished, try writing each of them an email (or some old-fashioned snail mail!) to tell them how grateful you are for them.

_____

_____

_____

_____

_____

_____

_____

_____

_____

_____

_____

_____

_____

_____

_____

_____

_____

_____

_____

_____

_____

_____

It is only with gratitude that life becomes rich.

DIETRICH BONHOEFFER

What is the nicest thing someone has done for you in the past week? Write it down here. Write about how the person's gesture made you feel. When you finish, try writing a post about it on social media and tagging the person in it, telling him or her how grateful you are for his or her kindness.

_____

_____

_____

_____

_____

_____

_____

_____

_____

_____

_____

_____

_____

_____

_____

_____

_____

_____

_____

_____

_____

_____

Appreciation is a wonderful thing. It makes what is excellent in others belong to us as well.

VOLTAIRE

Write down the names of three people whom you see regularly below. Next to each of their names write down one thing that you appreciate about that person. When you're finished, think about texting each person to express your gratitude. Or, even better, tell him or her in person the next time you get together.

_____

_____

_____

_____

_____

_____

_____

_____

_____

_____

_____

_____

_____

_____

_____

_____

_____

_____

_____

_____

_____

_____

When things aren't going great for me I tend to:

_____

_____

_____

_____

_____

_____

_____

_____

_____

When I rely on these habits to cope it makes me feel:

_____

_____

_____

_____

_____

_____

_____

_____

_____

One new thing I'd like to try instead is:

_____

_____

_____

_____

_____

_____

_____

_____

_____

_____

I think this new coping mechanism will help me practice gratitude during hard times because:

_____

_____

_____

_____

_____

_____

_____

_____

_____

_____

Have you ever asked or wished for something and then received WAY MORE than you expected? What feelings did that bring out in you? Write down some thoughts of gratitude for that experience right now.

Once I had asked God for one or two extra inches in height, but instead he made me as tall as the sky, so high that I could not measure myself.

MALALA YOUSAFZAI

Think about your living room in your apartment, condo, or house. List all of the things that you have to be thankful for in that room. Maybe you have a TV on which to watch your favorite shows with your partner or roommates, a couch to lounge and relax on, or cute decor that gives your space character.

_____

_____

_____

_____

_____

_____

_____

_____

_____

_____

_____

_____

_____

_____

_____

_____

_____

_____

_____

_____

_____

_____

_____

If you want the RAINBOW, you gotta put up with the RAIN.

DOLLY PARTON

Have you ever had a season of your life that felt really terrible, but turned out to be amazing? Write about both the "rain" and the "rainbow." How do you think the difficult parts of your experience prepared you to accept the good that came out of it? How did it change you for the better?

_____

_____

_____

_____

_____

_____

_____

_____

_____

_____

_____

_____

_____

_____

_____

_____

_____

_____

_____

_____

_____

_____

Ever have a hard time falling asleep? It seems like we all do at one time or another. Try using gratitude to slow down your breathing, provide instant stress relief, and help you finally doze off. Below, make a list of as many things as you can think of that bring you comfort, peace, and relaxation (a soft T-shirt, a scented candle, a favorite pillow, etc.). Refer to this list on nights when it's difficult to sleep.

Being grateful requires keeping your hands open for when the universe decides to drop a happy surprise into them.

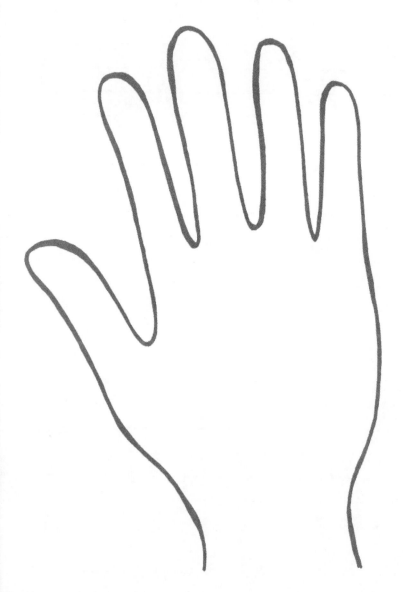

Write down some things (big or small) that have been recent "happy surprises" in the open hands.

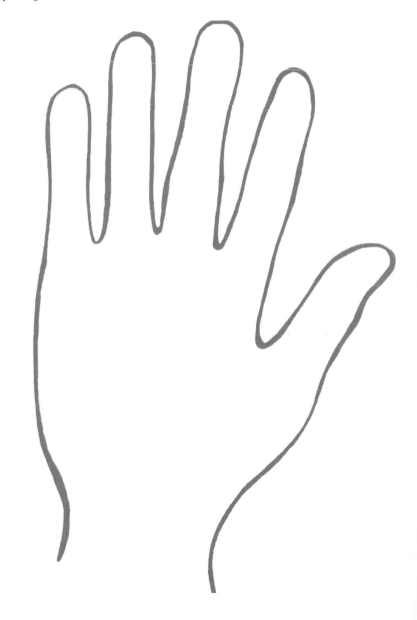

Who are some people whom you see or interact with nearly every day but don't know at all? A barista at your local coffee shop? A security guard at work? Write down as many people as you can think of. Next, write about how each person makes your life easier or something he or she does that just makes you smile. Then write down a way that you could show your gratitude next time you see that person.

_____

_____

_____

_____

_____

_____

_____

_____

_____

_____

_____

_____

_____

_____

_____

_____

_____

_____

_____

For me, every hour is grace. And I feel GRATITUDE In my HEART each time I can meet someone and look at his or her → smile.

ELIE WIESEL

When I look back in five years, the good things I'll remember about this time in my life are...

_____

_____

_____

_____

_____

_____

_____

_____

_____

_____

_____

_____

_____

_____

_____

_____

_____

_____

_____

_____

_____

_____

Gratitude is looking on the brighter side of life, even if it means hurting your eyes.

ELLEN DEGENERES

What about practicing gratitude feels challenging? What are some things that you have to give up or let go of when you decide to choose gratitude instead? What specific improvements have you noticed in your life as a result of taking on these challenges?

It's easy to feel down about the state of the world. Sometimes it can feel like all we hear is bad news. What is one good story you've heard about—maybe on the news, a podcast, or a talk show—that's happening in the world right now? How does this particular story help you to choose gratitude over despair?

Social media can be a blessing and a curse. There can sometimes be so much negativity in our feeds, but there can also be some examples of really beautiful friendship, community, and support. Write down three positive things that you've seen on social media recently. Maybe a friend posted something nice about another friend? Or a really uplifting news story?

Keep your eyes open to your mercies... The man who forgets to be grateful has fallen asleep in life.

ROBERT LOUIS STEVENSON

Even though it wasn't perfect, I'm grateful for my childhood because:

_____

_____

_____

_____

_____

My parent(s) made it possible for me to:

_____

_____

_____

_____

I was always able to:

_____

_____

_____

_____

I got to spend my free time:

_____

_____

_____

_____

_____

Being a child in my family taught me:

_____

_____

_____

_____

One special thing my family always made a priority was:

_____

_____

_____

_____

_____

Every Moment is a
GOLDEN ONE
for him who has the
VISION to recognize
it as such.

HENRY MILLER

Walk to a nearby window and look outside for a few minutes. What do you see? Try to see the beauty out there, even in the things that you don't usually consider beautiful. Powerful rain falling and watering the grass and trees. A neighbor greeting a stranger with a smile. Write it all down. And remember that there's beauty in all of it.

Can you remember a time in your life when everything seemed to be working out for you? What do you remember about that time? How did you feel? How did that experience shape you, and what lessons did you learn from feeling so content?

_____

_____

_____

_____

_____

_____

_____

_____

_____

_____

_____

_____

_____

_____

_____

_____

_____

_____

_____

_____

_____

_____

_____

Magnanimous means "especially generous, forgiving, or charitable." Who is someone in your life whom you've had to forgive? Write about the situation. Was it difficult to forgive him or her? What do you think you may have learned or gained by giving this person your forgiveness?

_____

_____

_____

_____

_____

_____

_____

_____

_____

_____

_____

_____

_____

_____

_____

_____

_____

_____

_____

_____

_____

_____

_____

Be about
TEN TIMES
more magnanimous
than you believe
yourself capable of.
Your life
will be a
HUNDRED TIMES
better for it.

CHERYL STRAYED

List five dreams of yours that haven't come true yet. Can you express some gratitude for them even though they haven't happened yet? Maybe you can be thankful for small steps you're taking that are getting you there. Or maybe you can be thankful that those dreams are just keeping you going through your day-to-day life. Write down a few thoughts of gratitude below your list.

In one jar below write three goals that you're working toward. The job of your dreams? Finding a better apartment? Repairing a broken relationship? In the other jar write three things to be thankful for right now, as you pursue those goals. Maybe something like, "I have a job that pays the bills" or "I have a roof over my head and a bed to sleep in."

Be happy with what you have while working for what you want.

HELEN KELLER

When I think about my family, I can be thankful that:

_____

_____

_____

_____

_____

_____

_____

_____

They always know how to:

_____

_____

_____

_____

_____

_____

_____

_____

_____

The values they have instilled in me are:

_____

_____

_____

_____

_____

_____

_____

_____

They make my life better by:

_____

_____

_____

_____

_____

_____

_____

_____

_____

Who,
being LOVED,
is poor?

OSCAR WILDE

What thoughts or feelings come to mind when you think of the word *beautiful*? Try to think of nonphysical characteristics that are beautiful to you. Maybe things like "strength" or "perseverance" or "a sense of humor." Write down some inner-beauty characteristics that you see in yourself, and show yourself some gratitude.

_____

_____

_____

_____

_____

_____

_____

_____

_____

_____

_____

_____

_____

_____

_____

_____

_____

_____

_____

_____

Write down three hopes that you have for today. At the end of today, write a little note of gratitude next to each one, whatever the outcome. Maybe you can be grateful for a desired outcome. Maybe you can be grateful for a step you took in the right direction. Maybe you can be grateful just to be able to have hope.

_____

_____

_____

_____

_____

_____

_____

_____

_____

_____

_____

_____

_____

_____

_____

_____

_____

_____

_____

_____

_____

Write down three worries that are in your head right now, leaving a space between them. Then, underneath each worry, write down one related thing that you're thankful for. Maybe you're worried about getting all of your work done this week. You might be thankful that you have a job or that you get to go to school.

_____

_____

_____

_____

_____

_____

_____

_____

_____

_____

_____

_____

_____

_____

_____

_____

_____

_____

_____

_____

The secret of Happiness is to count your Blessings while others are adding up their Troubles.

WILLIAM PENN

Hop on the stress-relief coloring bandwagon and color in the pretty word "Blessed" on the next page. While you're coloring, try to think about the many blessings in your life.

_____

_____

_____

_____

_____

_____

_____

_____

_____

_____

_____

_____

_____

_____

_____

_____

_____

_____

_____

_____

_____

_____

Blessed

HAPPINESS

makes up in

HEIGHT

for what it lacks in

length.

ROBERT FROST

Write a letter to your future self, a year from now. Tell yourself all of the things that you appreciate about you right now.

Write down three things that you can be thankful for right when you wake up in the morning. One might be as simple as "a fresh start." Tomorrow morning, when you open your eyes, lie in bed for an extra minute. Try to think of three things right there, before you even get out of bed.

_____

_____

_____

_____

_____

_____

_____

_____

_____

_____

_____

_____

_____

_____

_____

_____

_____

_____

_____

_____

Three books that I'm grateful I've read are:

_____

_____

_____

_____

_____

_____

_____

_____

They've affected my life because:

_____

_____

_____

_____

_____

_____

_____

_____

_____

_____

_____

We can only be said to be alive in those moments when our hearts are conscious of our treasures.

THORNTON WILDER

One song or album that I'm especially grateful for at this time in my life is:

_____

_____

_____

_____

_____

_____

_____

_____

_____

_____

_____

_____

_____

_____

_____

_____

_____

_____

_____

_____

_____

_____

_____

_____

It's helping me get through because:

_____

_____

_____

_____

_____

_____

_____

_____

_____

_____

_____

_____

_____

_____

_____

_____

_____

_____

_____

_____

_____

_____

_____

_____

A grateful mind IS A great mind WHICH EVENTUALLY ATTRACTS TO ITSELF great things.

PLATO

One place I feel grateful to have traveled to is:

_____

_____

_____

_____

_____

_____

_____

_____

_____

It made an impression on me because:

_____

_____

_____

_____

_____

_____

_____

_____

_____

_____

_____

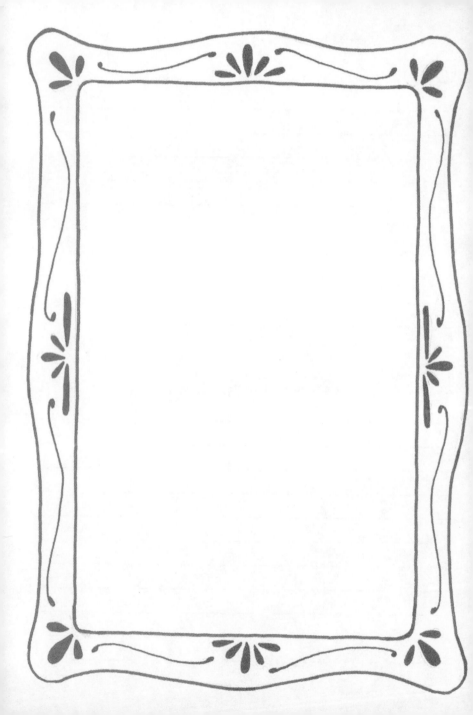

Sometimes our feelings can take over our day and make it seem like we don't have control over them. In the frame on the previous page, write down in your biggest, prettiest letters, "Today I choose happiness." Use colors, patterns, designs, and doodles, if you wish.

Our animal families are just as important as our people families. Write down some reasons you're grateful for a special animal in your life.

_____

_____

_____

_____

_____

_____

_____

_____

_____

_____

_____

_____

_____

_____

_____

_____

_____

_____

_____

_____

_____

_____

_____

_____

What expectations do you have for the next seven days? Write them down and try to think of how you can turn them into appreciation for whatever happens this week.

OUR GREATNESS has always come from people who EXPECT NOTHING and take NOTHING FOR GRANTED.

MICHELLE OBAMA

Count your rainbows, NOT your Thunderstorms.

About the Author

JENNY MECHER is the founder and designer behind ThreeLetterBirds, an online paper goods, lettering, and calligraphy shop. She lives in Chicago with her husband and two little girls, and does all of her design work from home in her cozy apartment near Wrigley Field.